SO-BMX-763

WE'VE GOT TO STOP MEETING LIKE THIS

by
Johnny Hart
&
Brant Parker

A FAWCETT GOLD MEDAL BOOK

Fawcett Publications, Inc., Greenwich, Connecticut

WE'VE GOT TO STOP MEETING LIKE THIS

Copyright © 1970, 1971 by Publishers Newspaper Syndicate

Copyright © 1975 by Fawcett Publications, Inc.

Published by special arrangement with Field Newspaper Syndicate

All rights reserved, including the right to reproduce this book or portions thereof in any form.

Printed in the United States of America

First printing: September 1975

1 2 3 4 5 6 7 8 9 10

6·17

8-13

8-19

8-29

8-31

9.2

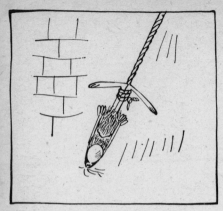

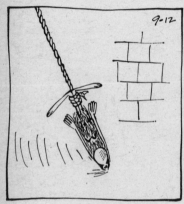

9-12

STOP...
STOP

9-19

I'VE BEEN
SAVED
BY THE
GOVERNOR?

YOU'VE BEEN
SAVED BY THE
ANTI-POLLUTION
LEAGUE.

9-23

ROBBING HOOD RETURNS!

A BAD DAY, BOSS?

A BAD DAY...

9-?

...I HELD UP A NUDIST COLONY.

9-29

THE YOUNGER GENERATION MUST STAND SHOULDER TO SHOULDER AND FACE THE FUTURE.

WHAT DOES **THAT** MEAN?

IT MEANS THERE WON'T BE ROOM TO SIT DOWN.

10-3

10-6

10-22

11-9

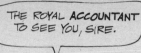

11-16

11-18

11-23

12.9

12-19

SIR RODNEY HAS COMPLETED A POLL ON YOUR POPULARITY...

12-22

... HE INTERVIEWED 112 PEOPLE.

WHY ISN'T RODNEY MAKING THIS REPORT HIMSELF?

HE'S IN THE HOSPITAL WITH 112 BLACK EYES.

VOMP

SNAP

12-25

PREPARE
TO MEET
THY
DOOM!

1-4

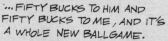

DO SOMETHING TO SPEED UP THESE PAYMENTS!

1-21

1-22

1-28

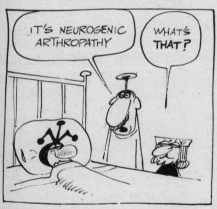

LOOK... THE KING IS GIVING THE PEASANTS THE OLE VICTORY SIGN.

2-26

THAT'S NO VICTORY SIGN...

... HE'S SHOWING THEM HOW THEY'LL LOOK HANGING IN IRONS.

3-1

3.6

And for more laughs, try...

THE WIZARD OF ID/YIELD   M3334

and in the B.C. series

B.C.–DIP IN ROAD   M3319

WHAT'S NEW, B.C.?   M3333

HURRAY FOR B.C.   M3323

FAWCETT

Only 95¢ Each Wherever Paperbacks Are Sold

If your bookdealer is sold out, send cover price plus 35¢ each for
postage and handling to Mail Order Department, Fawcett Publications, Inc., P.O. Box 1014, Greenwich, Connecticut 06830. Please
order by number and title. Catalog available on request.